The PIRATE QUEEN

Bradán

Text by David Ross
Illustrated by Tony O'Donnell

© 2002 Waverley Books Ltd

Published for Waverley Books Ltd by Geddes & Grosset,
David Dale House, New Lanark, ML11 9DJ, Scotland

ISBN 1 902407 24 5

Printed and bound in China

The PIRATE QUEEN

CHAPTER ONE: CLEW BAY

IMAGINE yourself on the open top of a high stone tower. Around you are the grey walls of a castle, built on the edge of steep cliffs. Out in front stretches a grey sea. Clouds hang low and ragged, driven by a strong gusty wind. Sudden showers of rain sweep down. All you can hear is the moan of the wind round the tower, and the crash of the waves on the rocks below. You are shivering with cold. You pull your damp woollen cloak around your shoulders. Your legs and feet are wet and chilled but you dare not leave your place. You are there as a look-out, gazing out to sea, for whatever comes in sight. Some days you are there from dawn to dusk, and see nothing but the empty waves. But not today.

Far out, something is there. Straining your eyes into the wind, you see a ship, two-masted, with a high stern. She has few sails set, for the wind would blow her where she does not want to go, closer in to this wild coastline. Many a fine vessel has perished on the reefs or against these wave-beaten cliffs. And there are other dangers for the seamen – pirates!

You are a pirate yourself, or at least, a pirate's child. Now, in a hurry, you pull up the hatch in the stone deck of the tower and swing your legs down, feeling for the rope-ladder. Already you are shouting:

"A ship! A ship!"

There is a stir of movement below. Orders are shouted. Feet pound on stone floors. A door, far off, slams shut.

In a few minutes, her oars thrust out like the legs of some great water beetle,

the galley is moving out through the bay. It is a heavy pull, into the wind, but the rowers are strong and keen. The merchant ship sees her, and sails are hoisted in a desperate effort to get away. Still, steadily the galley creeps closer. Back in your place on top of the tower, shading your eyes against the wind-flung rain, you watch as the two ships meet.

Though it's too far to see, you know what is happening. As the two vessels bump together, rolling in the waves, armed men spring to the sides of the merchant ship and clamber on board – too many of them for the crew to resist. The captain will be given a choice – pay a large amount of money, or have his ship emptied of its goods. If he refuses to pay, anything that can be removed is passed down to the rocking galley. For the captain,

the most surprising thing is that the pirate band is led by a woman. With mocking farewells, the pirates swing themselves down to their boat, leaving the frightened and furious sailors to struggle on to Galway harbour. There they will report to the English commander that once again the Pirate Queen has robbed one of the ships of the Queen of England.

The castle is on Clare Island, in Clew Bay. In this windy, rain-swept place, you live packed in with a hundred or more people. Others live around, in cabins on the island. Among their families are many bold men, ready to venture the dangerous sea, or to wield a sword in battle. But their chief is not a man, but a woman: the Pirate Queen, Grainne O'Malley.

CHAPTER TWO: HOW THE PIRATE QUEEN GOT HER NAME

GRAINNE (pronounced Grawn-ya) was born with the sea in her blood. For hundreds of years, the O'Malleys had been sailing from the west coast of Ireland. They went north to Scotland and south to Spain. Wool and fish, and sometimes gold from the Irish hills, were exchanged for wine, cloth, and weapons. But, out on the lawless seas, they were also buccaneers. Their galleys could sail faster and turn more easily than a merchant ship. With English settlers and soldiers pushing their way into Ireland, and claiming all Ireland as part of their own queen's domain, there were many among the Irish who thought it their duty to resist them.

Grainne's father, Owen O'Malley, was a chieftain among the Irish, and one of the leading men of Connaught. People called him Dubhdarra, meaning "black oak". He was a strong, dark-haired man, a natural leader, and proud to keep up the old style of the O'Malleys. His daughter was as strong-willed as himself. She

longed to travel on one of the O'Malley ships to some far-off place. As she got older she pestered her father to allow her to go.

"The sea is no place for a girl," he said.

"If I was a boy, would you take me?" she asked, and he said:

"Yes."

Her mother was angry.

"You are not a boy, but the daughter of a chief," she said. "A young lady you should be, as good as any in Ireland, not wanting to share the lives of vagabond sailors."

Grainne was not to be put off. She went to her room and cut off her long black hair, until her head was close-cropped, like a boy's. Wearing boy's clothes she came back to her parents.

"Now will you take me?" she said. Owen Dubhdarra could not refuse such spirit. So Grainne's seafaring life began, and when people called her Grainne Mhaol, or "Bald Grace", she did not mind. Soon it became a single name – Granuaile (pronounced Grawn-walya).

GRAINNE was married when she was hardly more than sixteen. Even then, it took a bold man to be her husband. He was Donal O'Flaherty, in line to be head of his clan, and his nickname was Donal of the Battles. He and Grainne had three children, Owen, Murrough and Margaret. Their life was not a peaceful one. Donal did not get his nickname for nothing, and they were usually in conflict with the merchants of Galway. When they were refused permission to use Galway harbour and its trading houses, the O'Flaherties traded on their own, sending ships far and wide, and felt free to plunder the shipping that used Galway. In all their battles and encounters, Grainne was as likely to be seen as Donal.

Donal met his death fighting another western clan, the Joyces, for possession of an island castle, but Grainne rallied his men and they fought off the attack. The castle was named Hen's Castle in her honour, and she put her own people to live there.

CHAPTER FOUR: THE DARK LADY OF DOONA

AFTER Donal's death, Grainne set up her headquarters on Clare Island. One day, news was brought of a ship that had run ashore not far away, close to Achill Island. Grainne and her men put to sea, hoping to find something of value from the wreck. But the ship had broken up by the time they reached the place, and its cargo was at the bottom of the sea. The only person saved from the wreck was a young man, Hugh de

Lacy. He was half-drowned, bruised and battered, but in the castle on Clare Island he was well looked after and soon restored to health. Hugh was a handsome young man, and he and Grainne fell in love. But he was killed, out on a deer-hunt on the mainland, by some of the MacMahons. Grainne's vengeance was swift. She caught and killed those who had slain Hugh, and took over their castle of Doona, overlooking Blacksod Bay. This exploit got her another name, "the Dark Lady of Doona".

RICHARD-AN-IARAINN, "Iron Dick", was her second husband. With this marriage, she secured his castle of Rockfleet and was then the mistress of the whole wide sweep of Clew Bay. She and Dick had one child, Tibbot-na-Long, or "Tibbot of the Ship". It is said that he got his name from being born on board one of his mother's ships, then on a voyage to Spain. When the ship was attacked by some rash pirates, Grainne rose from nursing her newborn infant to take command of the defence. She led her men aboard the other vessel, and herself slew their captain and won the day.

Another story tells how Grainne once gave seeds to her three sons to plant. The first two planted theirs carefully in the soil, but the third – perhaps Tibbot again – cast his into the sea, since that was the place where the O'Malleys' fortune had always come from. "You are my son," said Grainne.

By now she was famous. News of the Pirate Queen spread across Ireland and England. But to the English governors, she was a bandit and a criminal. They tried to get rid of her. Rockfleet castle was besieged by English ships, but Grainne led out her galleys in attack and the English ships were forced to flee.

But, as the English forces in Ireland grew stronger, Grainne's own chieftain, the O'Malley, head of the clan, was forced to submit, and to promise to accept English rule. If her chief submitted, Grainne had no choice but to follow. So she too appeared before the English governor at Galway, with Iron Dick beside her, and offered submission.

"A most famous feminine sea captain," he called her.

"I have three galleys and two hundred fighting men," declared Grainne. "They are now at your service wherever you command – in Scotland or Ireland."

But despite the offer, and the submission,

Grainne's life continued as before. Her sea raids and battles on land did not stop. There was no shortage of fights. She was now nearly fifty years of age, but that made no difference. On one occasion, when the O'Malleys were attacking the Stauntons of Kinturk Castle, her son Tibbot suddenly took fright and ran behind Grainne as she wielded her sword.

"Do you want to be a baby again?" she said, and shamed him into returning to the front of the fight.

AT LAST, leading a raid into the lands of the Earl of Desmond, Grainne was captured, and sent as a prisoner, first to Limerick, and then to Dublin Castle. That might have been the end of her, but by promising good behaviour, she was set free. Her husband, Iron Dick, may have helped. He was in the English government's good books and was soon to become The MacWilliam, chief of an important clan group. Back in Connaught, Grainne was now a great lady, but it was never enough for her to simply be someone's wife. When Iron Dick died, she returned to her native ground once again, and her old lifestyle started as before.

A new English governor was sent to Connaught. His name was Sir Richard Bingham, and he was determined to make this unruly province submit properly. Promises were not going to be enough this time. English troops patrolled through the mountains, and English ships cruised among the islands. Again Grainne was taken prisoner. Bingham threatened her with death, and many of her men, including her son Owen, were put to death. But Grainne survived, undaunted. When her other son, Murrough, sided with Bingham, she took her galleys across the bay to his house and burned it down.

SIR RICHARD BINGHAM and Grainne O'Malley were well-matched. Each made the other's life unbearable. But perhaps Grainne was beginning to tire of a life of constant strife. It was becoming more and more difficult for her to live as she had always done. English ships were too well-armed and English troops were too thick on the ground. She took a bold step. Disdaining the governor, she wrote directly to Queen Elizabeth in London.

"Your loyal and faithful servant Grany ne Mailly" was how she described herself. Grainne claimed that everything she had done was simply to protect herself and her people, because the queen's forces were not able to do so.

The queen wrote back, with a list of questions. Meanwhile, Bingham, who was determined to reduce all Connaught to English rule and English ways, continued to harass her. At last, Grainne decided to go to London herself.

Chapter Eight: The Pirate Queen and the Queen of England

HEARING of Grainne's decision to go directly to Queen Elizabeth, Bingham sent a letter to London calling Grainne a "notable traitor". If he hoped for her to be shut away in the Tower of London, he was to be disappointed.

Neither of these remarkable women was young. But Elizabeth was dressed splendidly, in a great spreading gown of heavily embroidered brocade, a red wig on her head, and her face heavily made up. Grainne's dress was plain country cloth, dyed saffron. But round her shoulders was a mantle of crimson velvet, and it was pinned by a golden brooch made by an Irish craftsman in far-off times. In her looks, she was no less regal than the English queen.

It was a strange meeting. Perhaps there were smart courtiers ready to titter at the uncouth dress and speech of the Irish chieftainess and her uneasy little group of followers. But none would have dared meet the flashing eye of either Grainne or their own queen. For between these two there was

an understanding. Both had ruled in a world of powerful, brawling, ambitious men. Their lives had been very different. Grainne's world was her cattle pastures, the torch-lit hall of a grey stone fortress, or the heaving deck of a boat. Elizabeth's was the glittering but often dangerous world of the royal court. In each, they were the rulers.

"I will fight in your quarrel with all the world," said Grainne.

Grainne left London to return to Connaught with the knowledge that her journey had been a triumphant success. Queen Elizabeth wrote to Sir

Richard Bingham with orders that did not please him. The Pirate Queen had found his queen's favour and there was nothing he could do about it. Indeed he was told to make sure that her sons provided for her and looked after her.

Even now, Grainne did not settle down to a quiet life. She was a fighter to the end. Returning to Ireland, she was refused admittance to Howth Castle by its governor. Grainne promptly seized the governor's young son, who was outside, and took him back to Mayo with her. He was only returned when his father promised that his gate would never again be shut against anyone seeking hospitality, and that an extra place would always be set at his table for the uninvited guest. This is still done in Howth Castle.

Grainne, the Pirate Queen has never been forgotten:

She had strongholds on her headlands
And brave galleys on the sea
And no warlike chief nor Viking
Had bolder heart than she.

Some Dates from the Life of Grainne O'Malley

1530	Grainne is born this year, or around it
1546	Grainne weds Donal O'Flaherty
1566	Grainne weds Richard an-Iarainn
1577	Grainne "submits" to the English governor at Galway
	In the same year, she is captured raiding against the Earl of Desmond
1581	Richard an-Iarainn becomes The MacWilliam
1583	Richard dies and Grainne returns to the O'Malley lands
1584	Sir Richard Bingham becomes governor of Connaught
1586	Grainne is captured for the second time, and released
1593	Grainne visits Queen Elizabeth in London
1603	Grainne dies sometime during this year